newton faulkner
hand built by robots

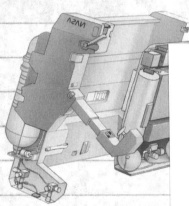

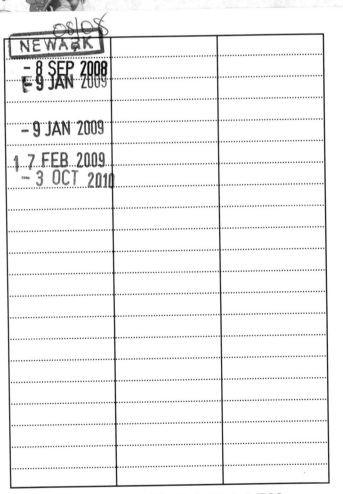

Nottinghamshire C

787. 6

Culture & Co

§

Wise Public
part of The Music S
London / New York / Paris / Sydney / Copen

**Nottinghamshire
County Council**

DP&P(O) 05.07/Comms/4261

Published by
Wise Publications
14-15 Berners Street, London, W1T 3LJ, UK.

Exclusive distributors:
Music Sales Limited
Distribution Centre, Newmarket Road,
Bury St Edmunds, Suffolk, IP33 3YB, UK.

Music Sales Pty Limited
20 Resolution Drive, Caringbah, NSW 2229, Australia.

Order No. AM992717   ISBN 978-1-84772-447-2

Edited by Tom Farncombe.
Music arranged by Arthur Dick.
Music processed by Paul Ewers Music Design.
Art direction & design by Steve Stacey.
Photography by Harry Woodd.
Printed in the EU.

Special thanks to Matt Buchanan for his help with proof-reading the arrangements.

www.musicsales.com

Dedicated to the memory of Eric Roche (1967 – 2005)
For more information about Eric Roche, please visit www.ericroche.com

Hello, and welcome to the *Hand Built By Robots* tab book.
The main thing I want to say is about the songs with percussive guitar parts ('Feels Like Home', 'Teardrop' etc).
Always start really slowly; work out which percussive hits land on the same beat as guitar notes and
which ones don't, and then start speeding it up. Please be careful! All guitars are different and will have
different sweet spots percussion-wise. It's not a case of 'the harder you hit it, the louder it'll be'.
You've got to hit in the right place in the right way and that is likely to be in a different place on different
instruments. The last thing I want is a bunch of people turning up to gigs with damaged guitars or
damaged limbs. Some of the movements required – for instance, the bass thump – are pretty strange,
and may take a bit of getting use to, so if anything starts hurting take a break.

If you like the style of these songs, check out Eric Roche and Thomas Leeb: they're my two favourite players.

That's about it. The only other thing you have to do is enjoy it!

Newton Faulkner, 2008

guitar tablature explained

Guitar music can be notated in three different ways: on a musical stave, in tablature, and in rhythm slashes.

RHYTHM SLASHES: are written above the stave. Strum chords in the rhythm indicated. Round noteheads indicate single notes.

THE MUSICAL STAVE: shows pitches and rhythms and is divided by lines into bars. Pitches are named after the first seven letters of the alphabet.

TABLATURE: graphically represents the guitar fingerboard. Each horizontal line represents a string, and each number represents a fret.

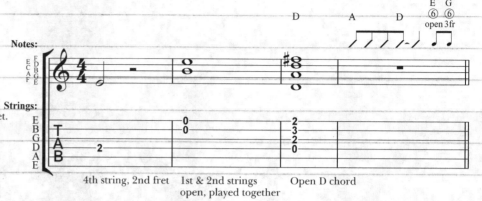

4th string, 2nd fret   1st & 2nd strings open, played together   Open D chord

definitions for special guitar notation

SEMI-TONE BEND: Strike the note and bend up a semi-tone (½ step).

WHOLE-TONE BEND: Strike the note and bend up a whole-tone (full step).

GRACE NOTE BEND: Strike the note and bend as indicated. Play the first note as quickly as possible.

QUARTER-TONE BEND: Strike the note and bend up a ¼ step

BEND & RELEASE: Strike the note and bend up as indicated, then release back to the original note.

COMPOUND BEND & RELEASE: Strike the note and bend up and down in the rhythm indicated.

PRE-BEND: Bend the note as indicated, then strike it.

PRE-BEND & RELEASE: Bend the note as indicated. Strike it and release the note back to the original pitch.

HAMMER-ON: Strike the first note with one finger, then sound the second note (on the same string) with another finger by fretting it without picking.

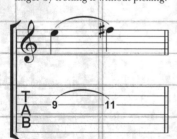

PULL-OFF: Place both fingers on the note to be sounded, strike the first note and without picking, pull the finger off to sound the second note.

LEGATO SLIDE (GLISS): Strike the first note and then slide the same fret-hand finger up or down to the second note. The second note is not struck.

SHIFT SLIDE (GLISS & RESTRIKE): Same as legato slide, except the second note is struck.

NATURAL HARMONIC: Strike the note while the fret-hand lightly touches the string directly over the fret indicated.

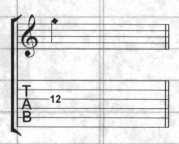

TAP HARMONIC: The note is fretted normally and a harmonic is produced by tapping the fret indicated in brackets (which will be twelve frets higher than the fretted note).

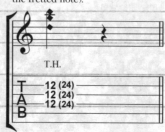

PALM MUTING: The note is partially muted by the pick hand lightly touching the string(s) just before the bridge.

MUFFLED STRINGS: A percussive sound is produced by laying the first hand across the string(s) without depressing, and striking them with the pick hand.

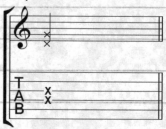

TRILL: Very rapidly alternate between the notes indicated by continuously hammering-on and pulling-off.

TAPPING: Hammer ('tap') the fret indicated with the pick-hand index or middle finger and pull-off to the note fretted by the fret hand.

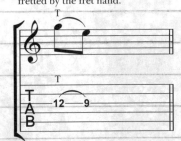

FINGER PICKING: Traditional notation for picking. p = thumb; i = first (index finger); m = middle finger; a = ring finger.

ARPEGGIATE: Play the notes of the chord indicated by quickly rolling them from bottom to top.

special percussive techniques

BASS THUMP: Strike body of guitar below sound-hole with the heel of the hand to create a deep, kick drum style thump.

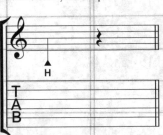

Hit on side of the body of the guitar with left (fretting) hand to create a sharp, high sound (the 'snare' response to the 'kick drum' effect on the left).

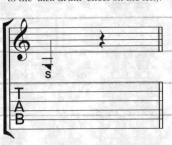

SLAP: Percussive, muted attack with thumb of picking hand.

Strike with fingers below sound-hole.

additional information

Newton Faulkner uses three guitars built by Nick Benjamin. These are:

1) A JOM (Jumbo Orchestra Model) in sitka spruce and mahogany with an LR Baggs Double-Barrel pickup system (pictured). This system uses an undersaddle pickup in the bridge, and an additional microphone inside the body of the guitar. This enables the percussive techniques outlined above to be heard on stage.

2) A reinforced prototype model originally built for Eric Roche. This is a cedar and mahogany Jumbo model with a Baggs M1 Dual-Source magnetic pickup and internal mic system and an RMC synth pickup system (not currently used live). This guitar also has a spruce scratchplate which allows the surface of the guitar to literally be scratched with the nails for a percussive effect without causing too much damage.

3) A JOM Scoop model, featuring the distinctive 'Benjamin Scoop' cutaway to facilitate upper-fret access, made of lutz spruce and palo escrito rosewood with a Baggs Element Dual-Source pickup and mic system.

The dual pickup systems allow for the separate mixing of the signal from the strings and the hits to the body; the guitars are usually plugged into and EQed by Highlander PAMDI (Pro Acoustic Mixer DI) direct boxes, also set up by Nick Benjamin.

For further information about Benjamin guitars, please visit www.benjaminguitars.co.uk

intro

Words & Music by Newton Faulkner

All Gtrs.
6 = D	3 = G
5 = G	2 = A
4 = D	1 = D

Capo 2nd Fret

Tune guitar down a further semitone to match recording.

♩ = 118 Freely

Gtr. 1 (acous.)

mf let ring…

Tab 0 = 2nd fret

♩ = 118 a tempo

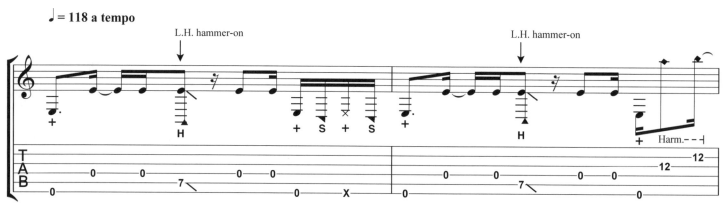

Percussive notation:
+ = thumb slap
H = strike body of guitar above sound hole with heel of the hand
S = L.H. hit on lower left side of guitar

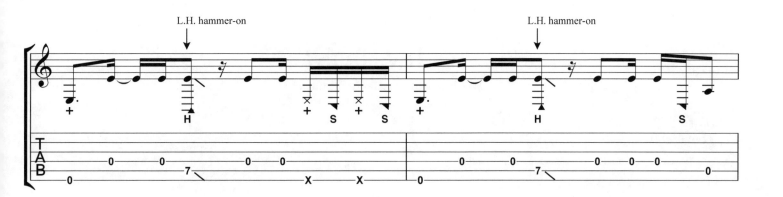

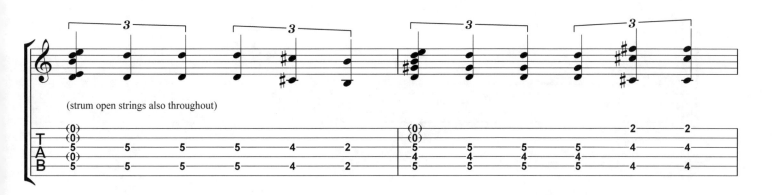

(strum open strings also throughout)

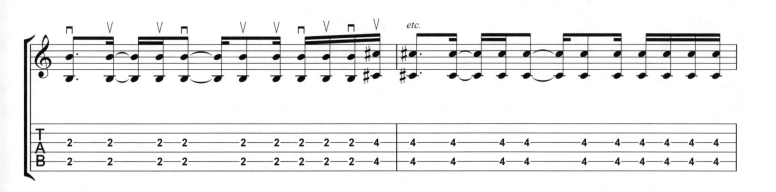

etc.

Segue

9

to the light

Words & Music by Newton Faulkner

Tune guitar down a further semitone to match recording.

♩ = 126

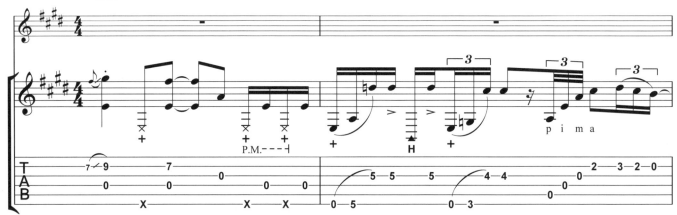

Percussive notation:

+ = thumb slap

H = strike body of guitar above sound hole with heel of the hand

Tab 0 = 2nd fret

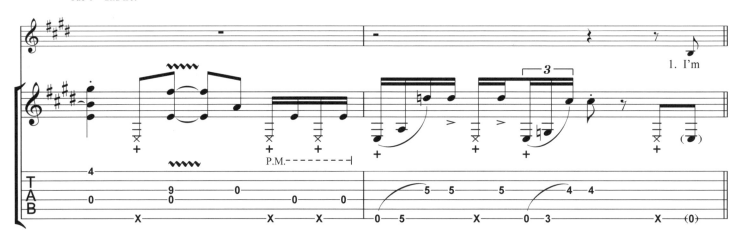

Verse

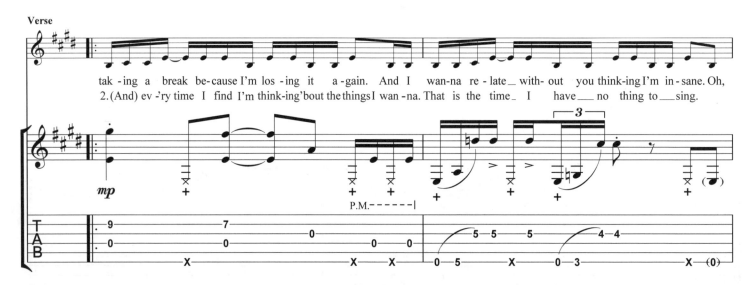

tak-ing a break be-cause I'm los-ing it a-gain. And I wan-na re-late__ with-out you think-ing I'm in-sane. Oh,
2.(And) ev -'ry time I find I'm think-ing 'bout the things I wan -na. That is the time__ I have__ no thing to __ sing.

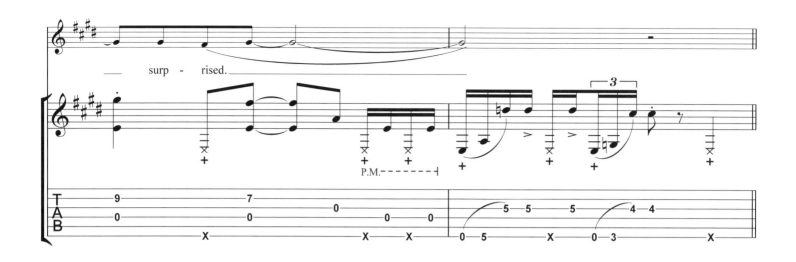

_____ surp - rised.

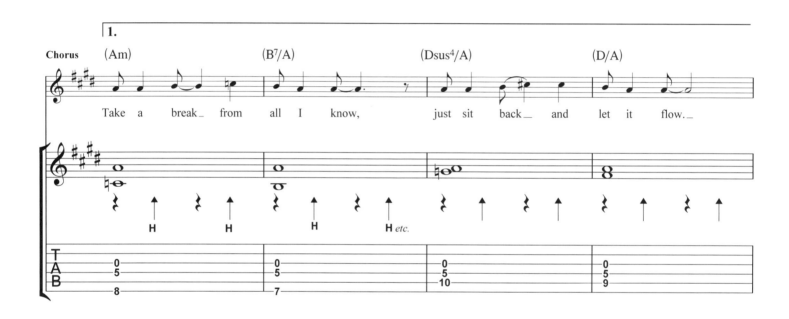

1.

Chorus (Am) (B7/A) (Dsus4/A) (D/A)

Take a break_ from all I know, just sit back_ and let it flow._

H   H   H   H etc.

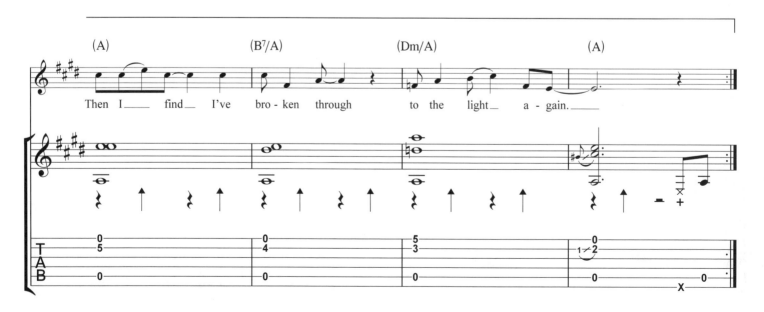

(A) (B7/A) (Dm/A) (A)

Then I_ find_ I've bro - ken through to the light_ a - gain._

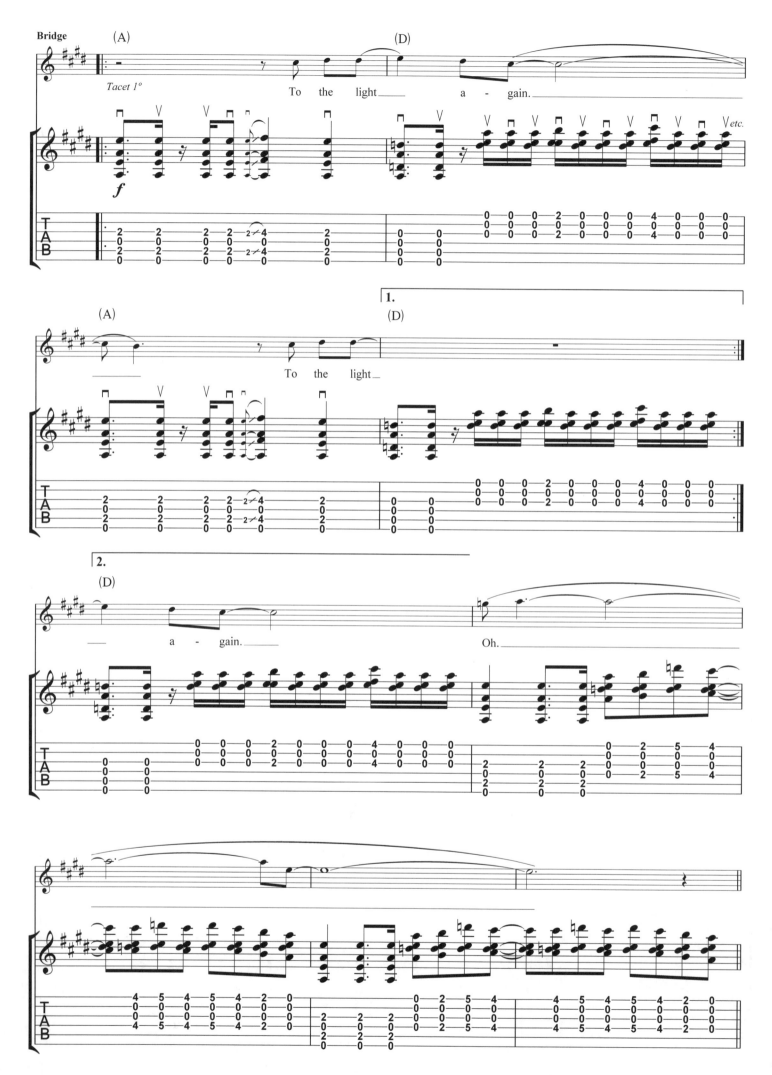

15

i need something

Words & Music by Newton Faulkner

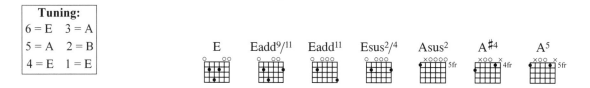

Tuning:
6 = E   3 = A
5 = A   2 = B
4 = E   1 = E

Tune guitar down a semitone to match recording.

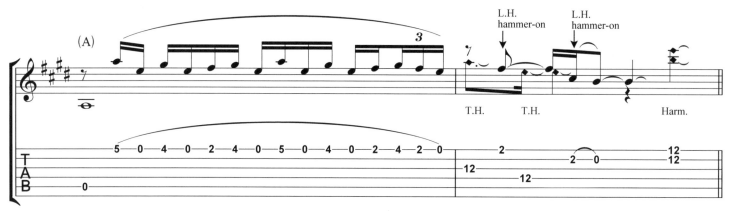

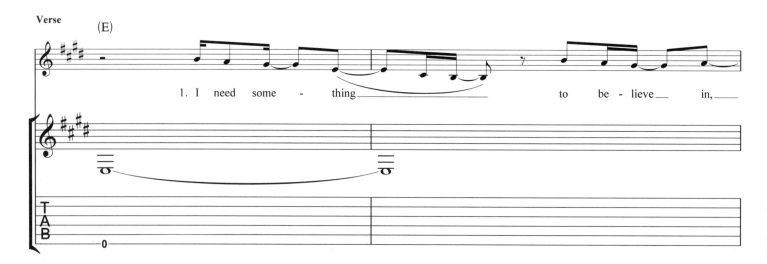

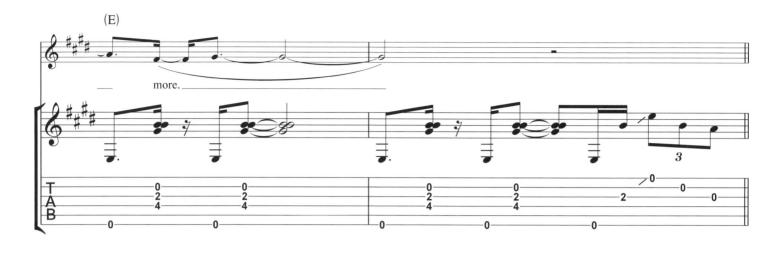

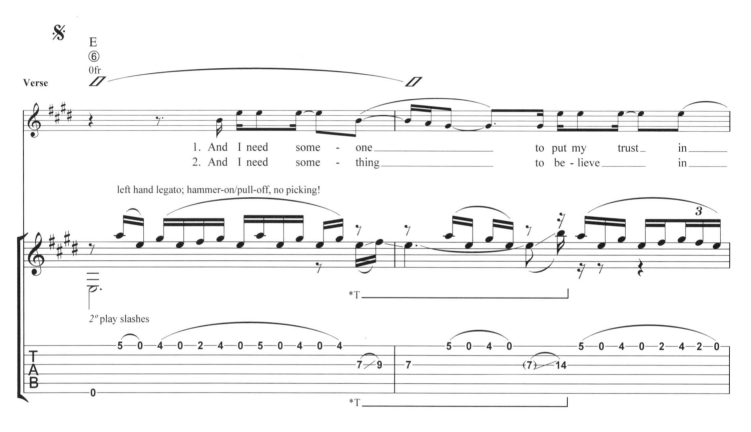

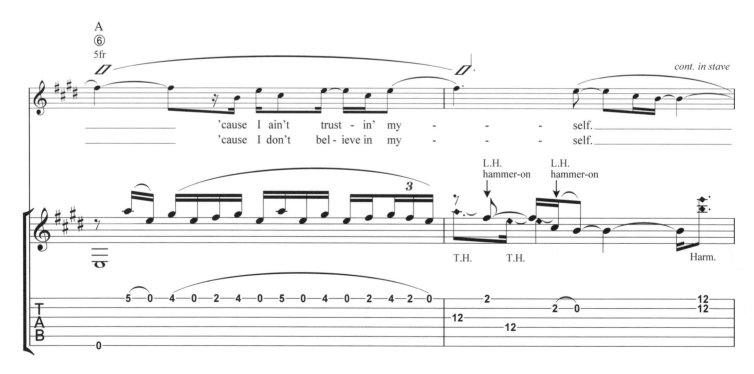

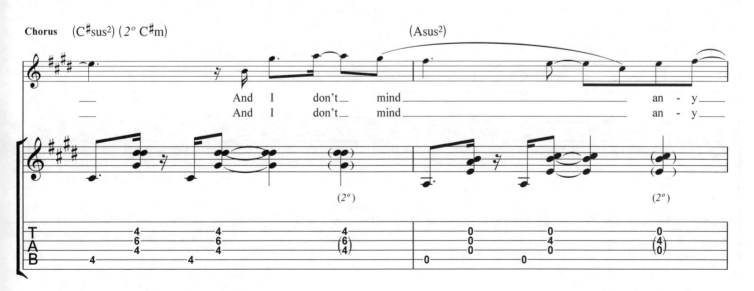

And I don't mind
And I don't mind

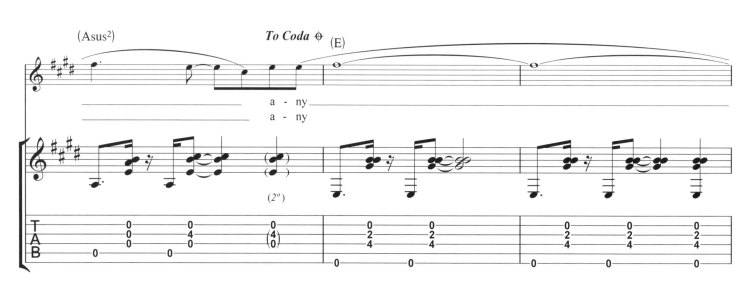

a - ny
a - ny

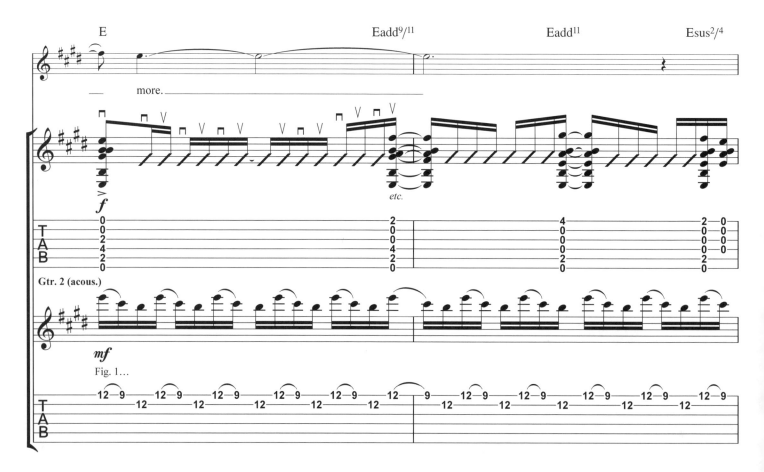

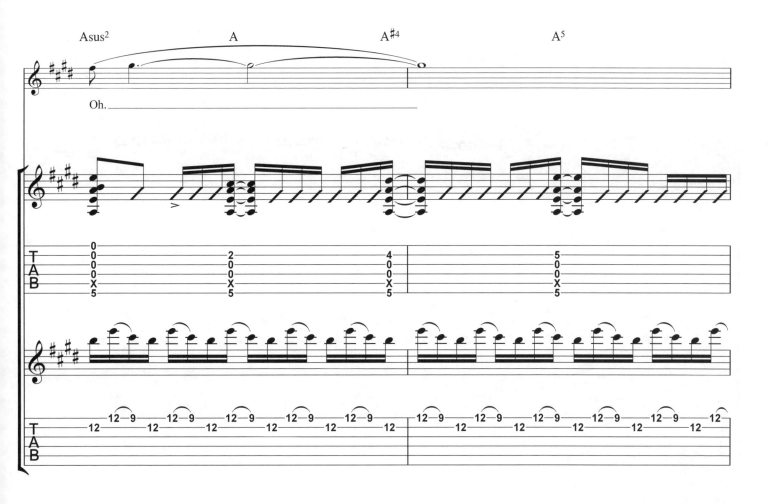

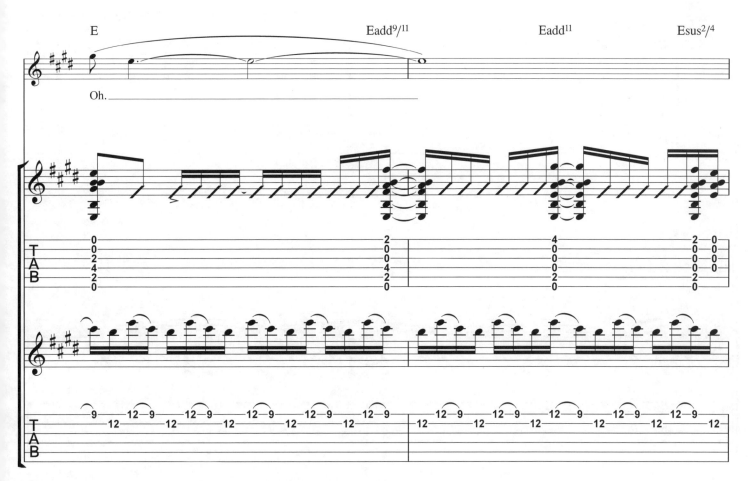

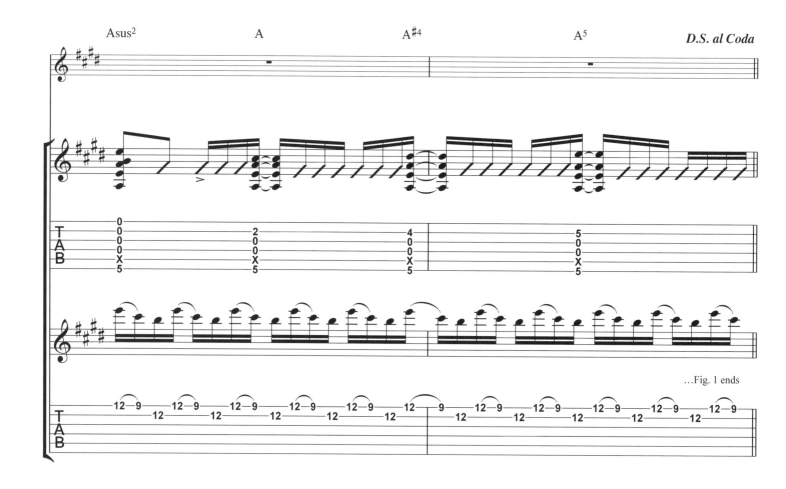

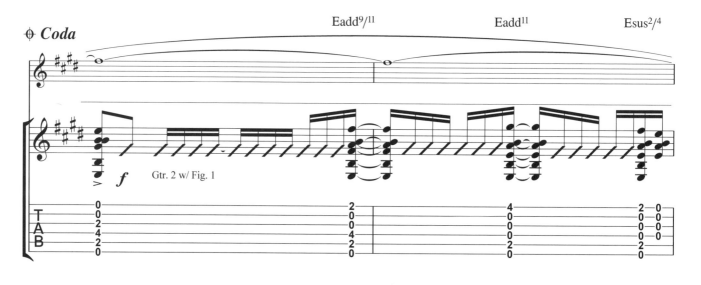

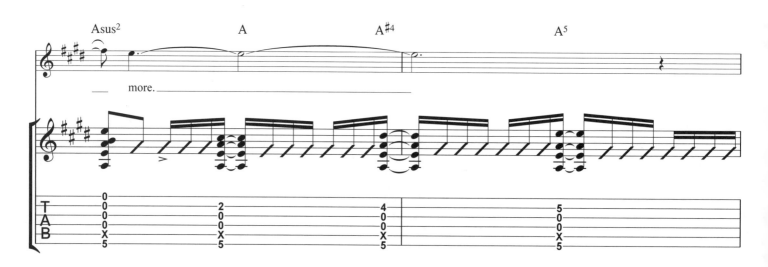

all i got

Words & Music by Newton Faulkner & Crispin Hunt

Standard tuning, Capo 7th fret

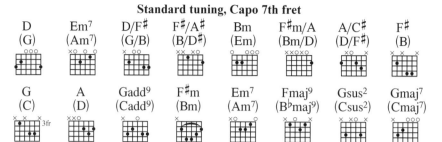

Tune guitar down a semitone to match recording.

Intro

♩ = 105

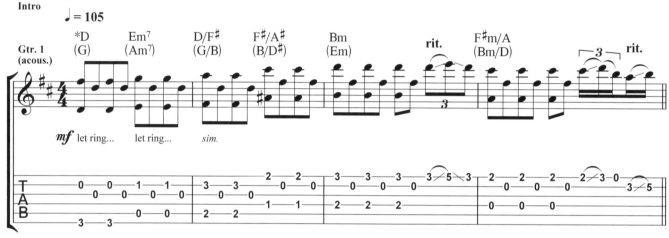

*Symbols in parentheses represent chord names with respect to capoed guitar (Tab 0 = 7th fret).
Symbols above represent actual sounding chords.

a tempo

1. And all I got-ta do___ is sit a-round and wait.___ And all I got-ta do___
2.(And) all I got-ta do___ is just hold back and___ wait. But ev-'ry-time I try___

26

dream catch me

Words & Music by Newton Faulkner, Crispin Hunt & Gordon Mills

30

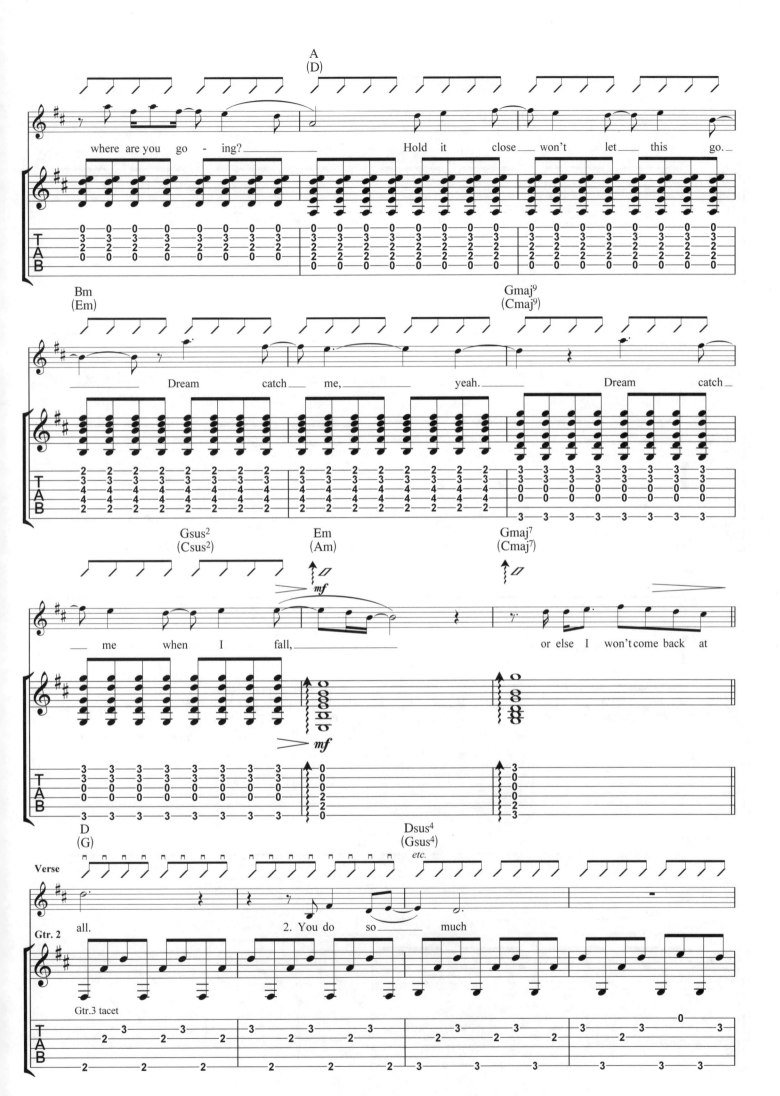

31

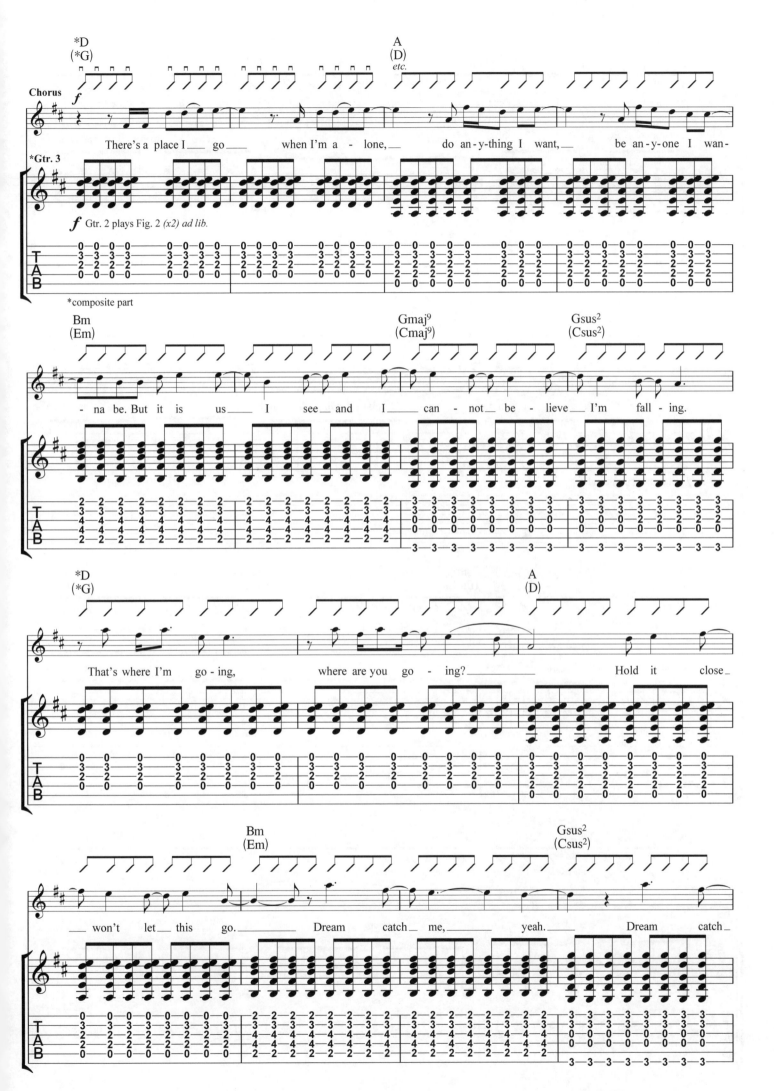

35

feels like home

Words & Music by Newton Faulkner

Tuning:
6 = E   3 = E
5 = G♯ 2 = B
4 = E   1 = E
Capo 4th fret

♩ = 100

Intro

N.C.

Gtr. 1 (acous.)

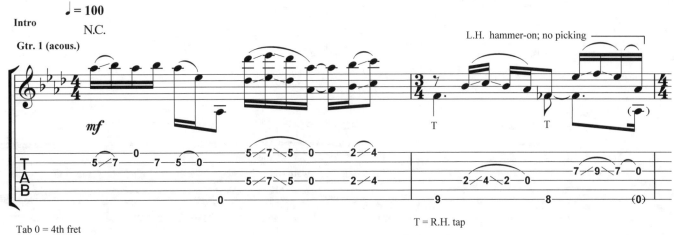

Tab 0 = 4th fret

T = R.H. tap

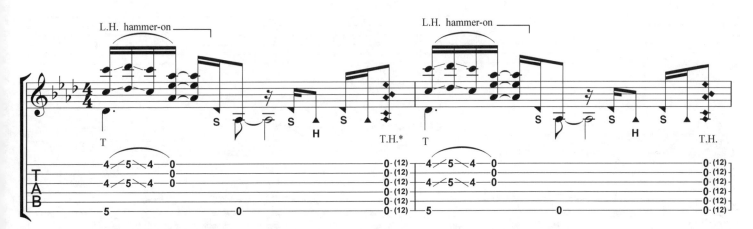

Percussive notation:
H = strike body of guitar above soundhole with heel of the hand
S = L.H. hit on lower left side of guitar

*Tap at 12th fret with flat of index finger
to produce harmonics

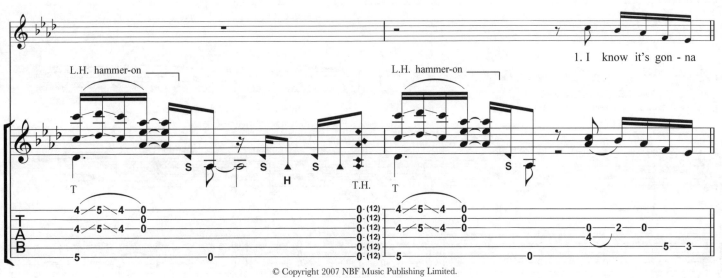

1. I know it's gon - na

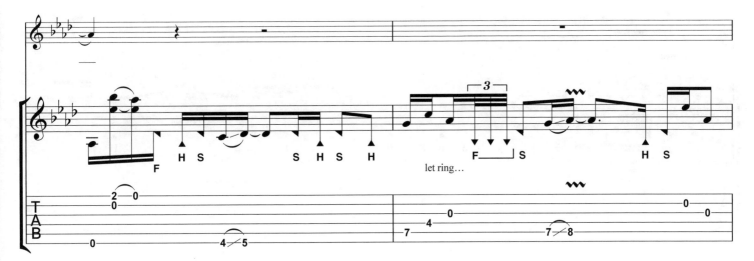

F = percussive hit w/right hand fingers below sound hole

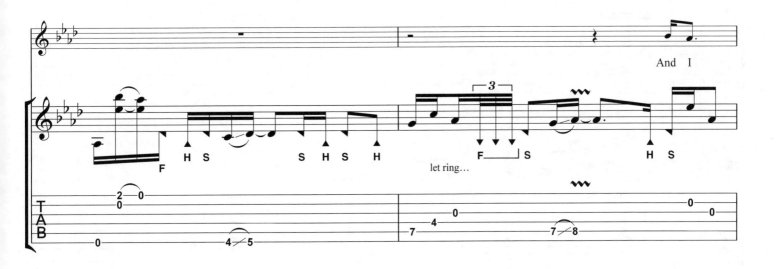

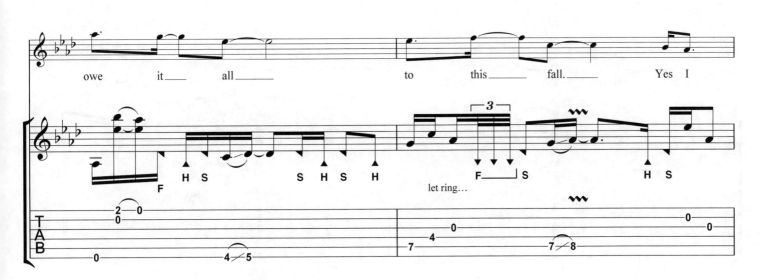

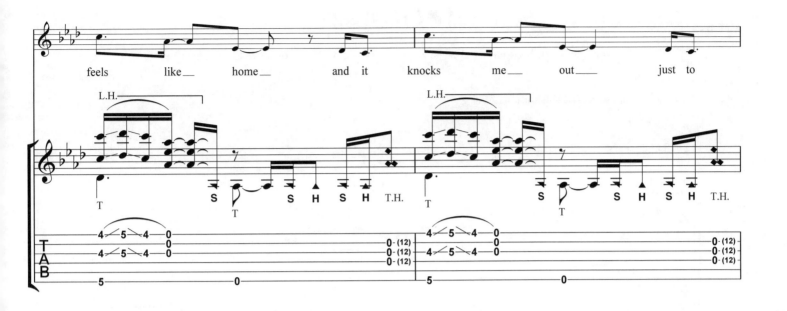

feels like   home   and it   knocks   me   out   just to

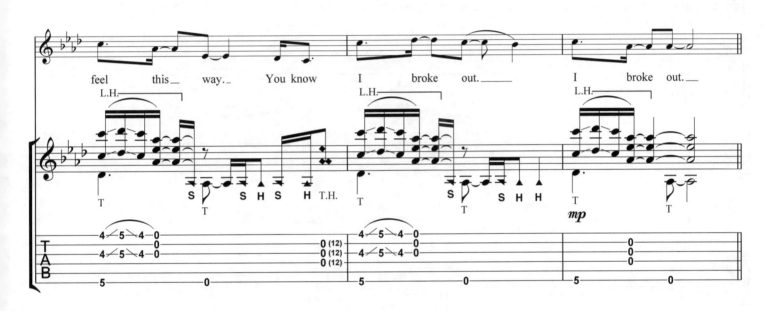

feel this   way.   You know   I   broke out.   I   broke out.

Repeat to fade

Outro

let ring…

43

teardrop

Words & Music by Robert Del Naja, Grant Marshall, Andrew Vowles & Elizabeth Fraser

Tune guitar down a further semitone to match recording.

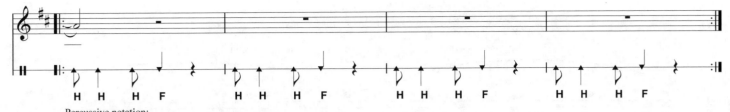

Percussive notation:
H = strike body of guitar above sound hole with heel of the hand
F = percussive hit with right hand fingers below sound hole

Verse

2. Wat - er is my eye.___ Most faith - ful___ mir - ror.___

Fig. 1

L.H hammer-ons;
no picking…

sim.

*R.H. strikes bass note on 1st beat of Fig. 1

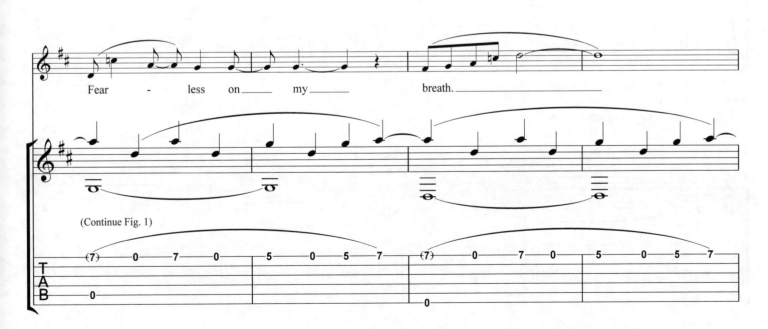

Fear - less on___ my___ breath.___

(Continue Fig. 1)

Tear - drop on the fire___ of a___ con - fess - ion.___

Fear - less on___ my___ breath.___

Most faith - ful___ mir - ror.___ Fear - less on___ my___

Harm.- - - - - - - - - - - - - -| Harm.- - - - - - - - - - - - - - - -|

rit.

breath.___ Tear - drop on the fire.___

tacet Fig.1

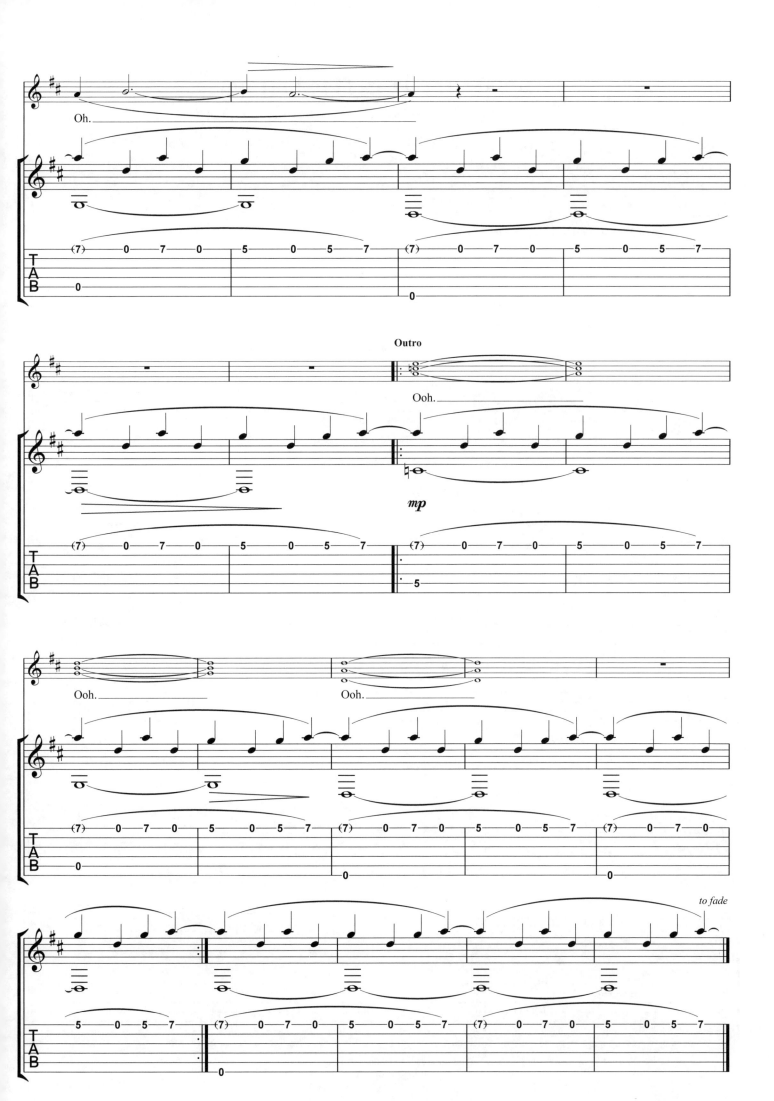

gone in the morning

Words & Music by Newton Faulkner & Toby Faulkner

Tuning:

6 = D	3 = G
5 = A	2 = A
4 = D	1 = D

Tune guitar down further semitone to match recording.

Intro

♩ = 130

Gtr. 1 (acous.)

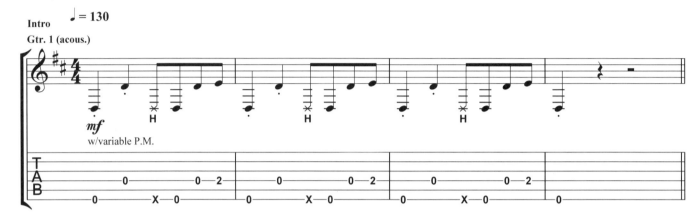

mf

w/variable P.M.

H = strike body of guitar above soundhole with heel of the hand

Verse

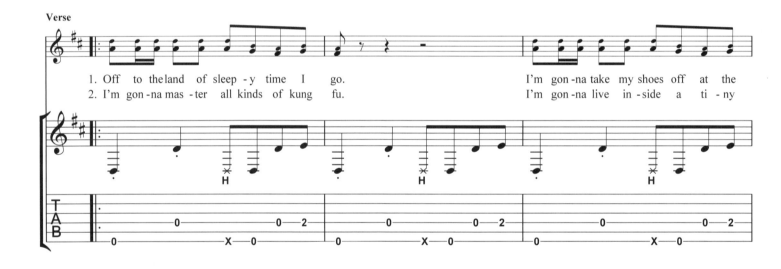

1. Off to the land of sleep-y time I go.   I'm gon-na take my shoes off at the
2. I'm gon-na mas-ter all kinds of kung fu.   I'm gon-na live in-side a ti-ny

door.   I'm gon-na go where dreams like ri-vers flow._____ Whoah.___
zoo.   I'm gon-na grow my-self a gi-ant af-ro (incredible). Whoah.___

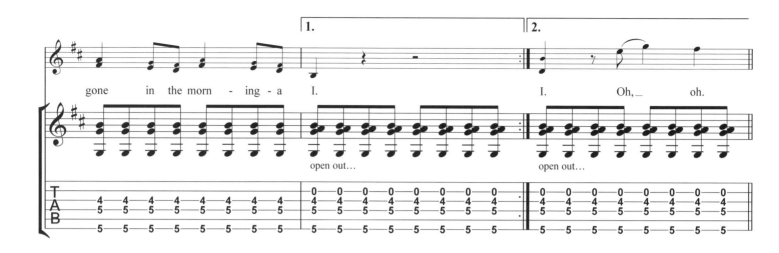

gone in the morn - ing - a I.   I. Oh,___ oh.

open out…   open out…

Bridge

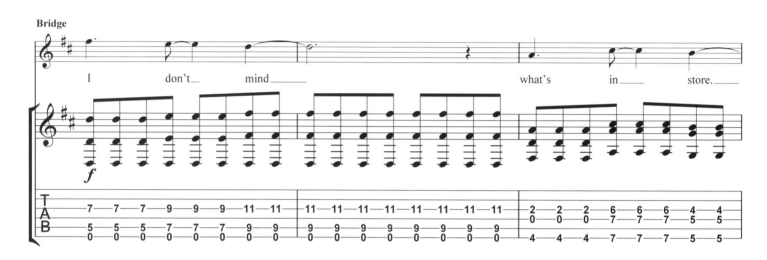

I   don't___   mind_____   what's   in ___   store.___

___   I'll make it in my own   sweet___   time,_____

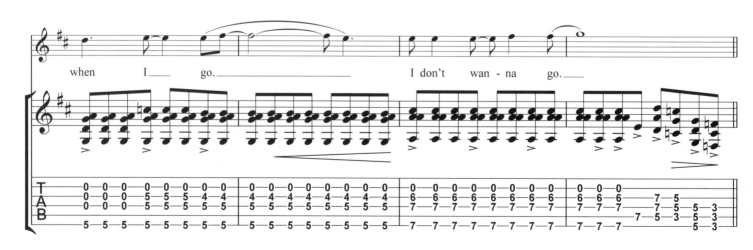

when   I___   go._____   I don't wan - na   go.___

53

sitar-y thing

Music by Newton Faulkner

Repeat to fade

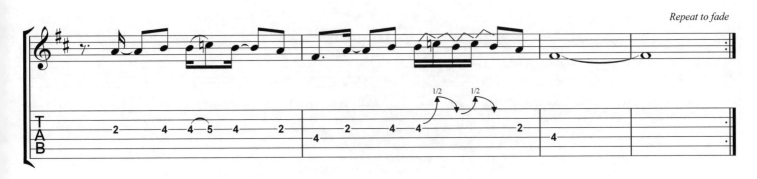

uncomfortably slow

Words & Music by Newton Faulkner & Adam Argyle

Standard tuning, Capo 2nd fret

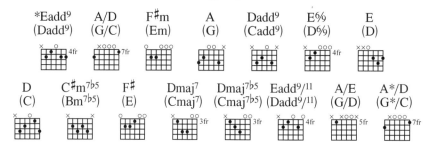

*Symbols in parentheses represent chord names with respect to capoed guitar.
Symbols above represent actual sounding chords.

1. Tra - vel - ling___ a - gain,___ I know ex - act - ly how___ it's gon - na end.___ The
2. Some - thing's got - ta change, I know I'm luck - y in___ a lot of ways. So

rou - tine day - dream starts as I___ get off.___ I'm
why do I want___ more than what I have?___

hold - ing up___ the queue___ be - cause my tick - et won't__ go through.___ I
Brace my - self to hear___ the lies, I won - der if___ they know___ that I don't

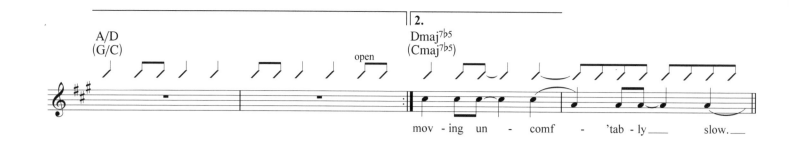

mov - ing un - comf - 'tab - ly____ slow.___

Middle

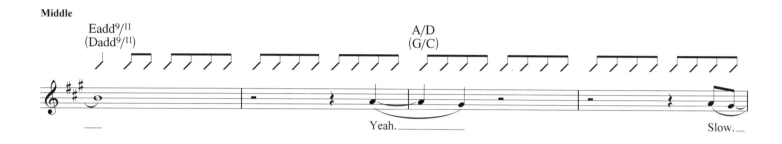

— Yeah.___ Slow.__

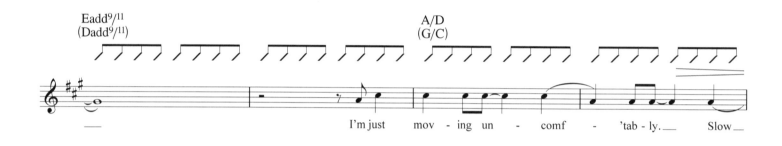

— I'm just mov - ing un - comf - 'tab - ly.__ Slow __

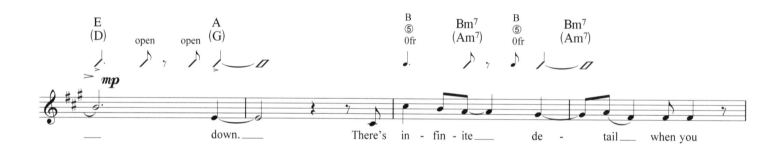

— down.___ There's in - fin - ite__ de - tail__ when you

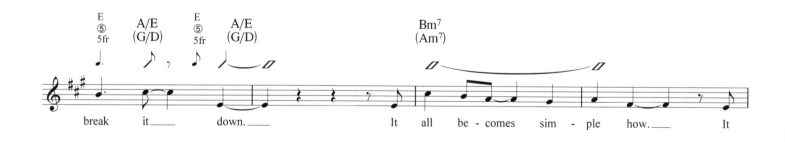

break it__ down.___ It all be - comes sim - ple how.__ It

Chorus

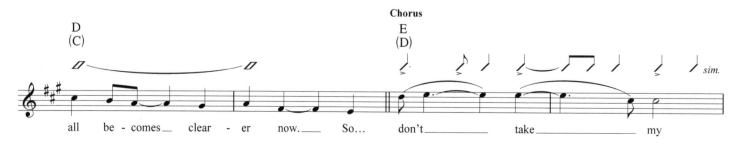

all be - comes__ clear - er now.__ So... don't_____ take_____ my

58

straight towards the sun

Words & Music by Newton Faulkner & Crispin Hunt

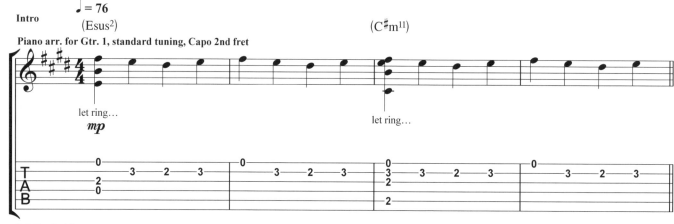

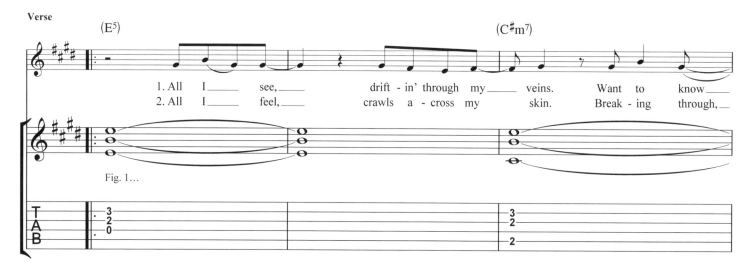

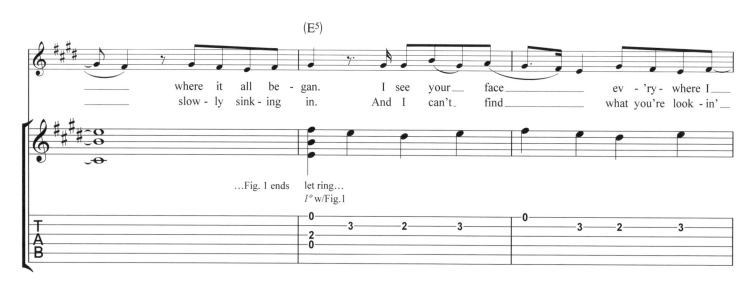

(C♯m⁷)   (A⁶)   (F♯m⁷)

__ turn.   Now I'm left__   e - ter - nal -ly__ to __   burn, __   e - ter - nal -ly __ to.
__ for.   Noth - ing's left, __   noth -ing's left at __   all, __   noth -ings left at. _

let ring…   (play 1° & 2°)

(E)   (Amaj⁷)   (E)   (Amaj⁷)

__ } When you're on   your   own, __   kill - ing   time. __   Want to make   it   right, _   make   it.

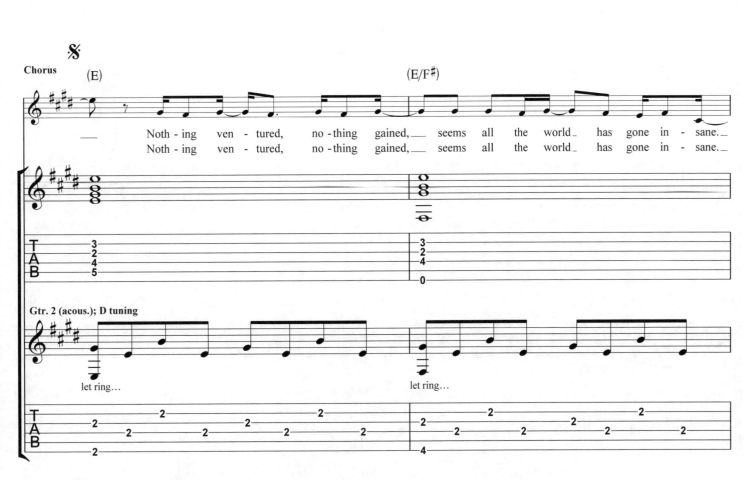

𝄋

Chorus

(E)   (E/F♯)

__ Noth - ing   ven - tured,   no -thing   gained, __   seems   all   the   world_   has   gone in - sane. __
__ Noth - ing   ven - tured,   no -thing   gained, __   seems   all   the   world_   has   gone in - sane. __

Gtr. 2 (acous.); D tuning

let ring…   let ring…

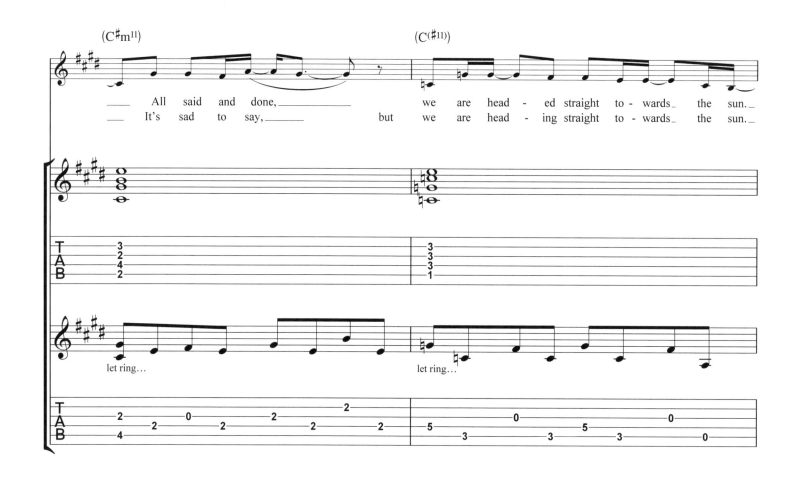

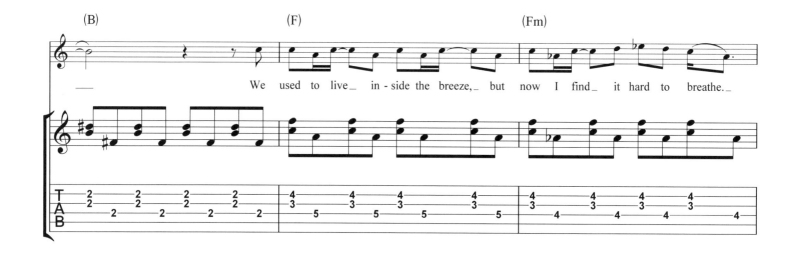

We used to live_ in - side the breeze,_ but now I find_ it hard to breathe._

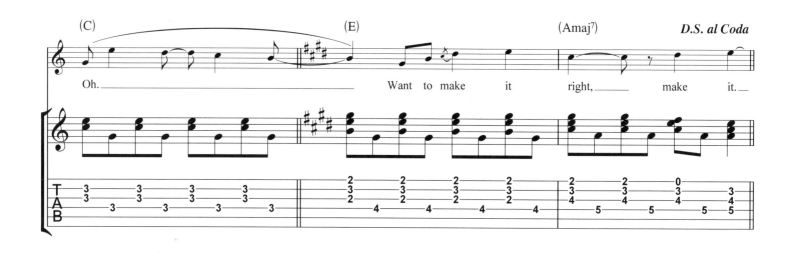

Oh._____ Want to make it right,_____ make it._

D.S. al Coda

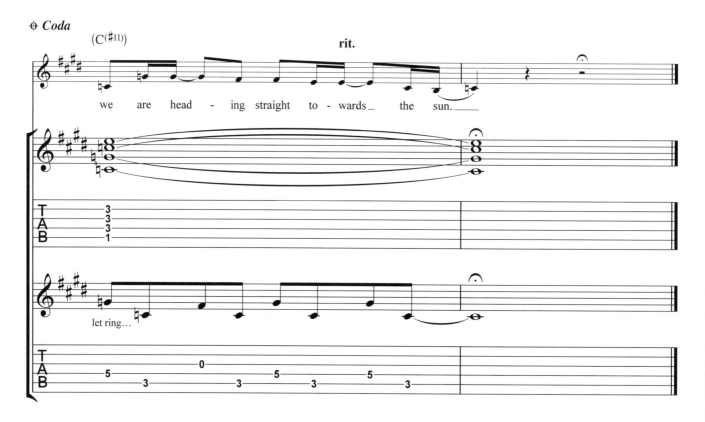

we are head - ing straight to - wards_ the sun._____

rit.

let ring…

people should smile more

Words & Music by Newton Faulkner, Adam Argyle & Crispin Hunt

Tune down a tone to match recording.

Intro ♩ = 88

Gtr. 1 (acous.); standard tuning

69

she's got the time

Words & Music by Newton Faulkner & Toby Faulkner

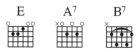

Intro ♩ = 190 (♫ = ♪³♪)

Gtr. 1 (Standard tuning; miniature nylon string acoustic – as battered as possible!)

Verse

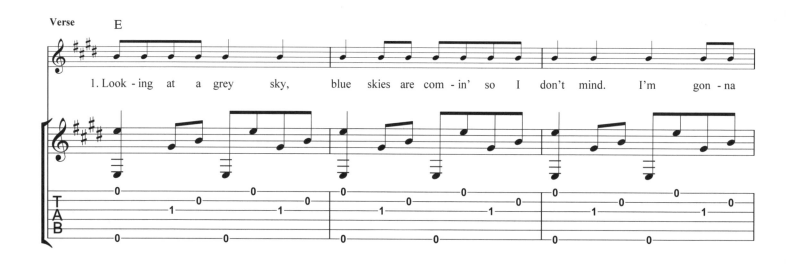

1. Look-ing at a grey sky, blue skies are com-in' so I don't mind. I'm gon-na

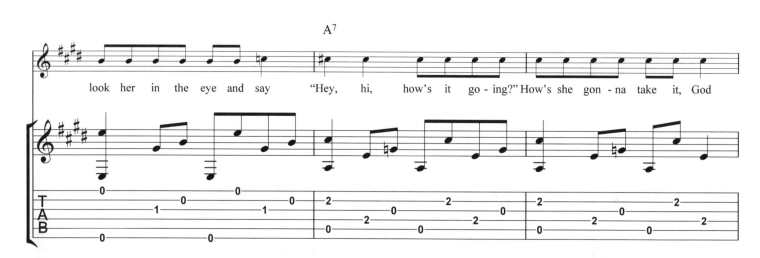

look her in the eye and say "Hey, hi, how's it go-ing?" How's she gon-na take it, God

U.F.O

Words & Music by Newton Faulkner & Toby Faulkner

Tuning:
6 = D   3 = G
5 = A   2 = A
4 = D   1 = D

*L.H mute /percussive R.H. stroke.

H = strike body of guitar above sound hole with heel of the hand

*L.H. mute /percussive R.H. stroke.

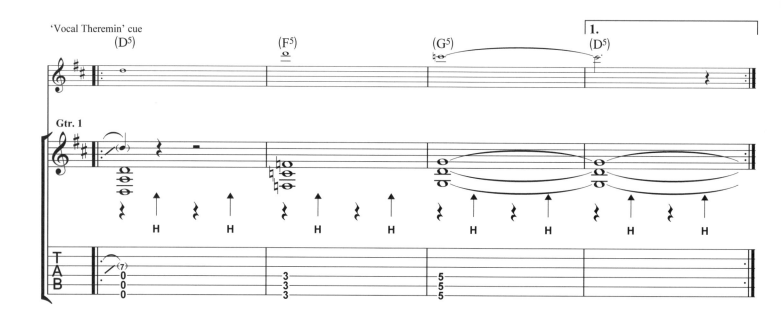

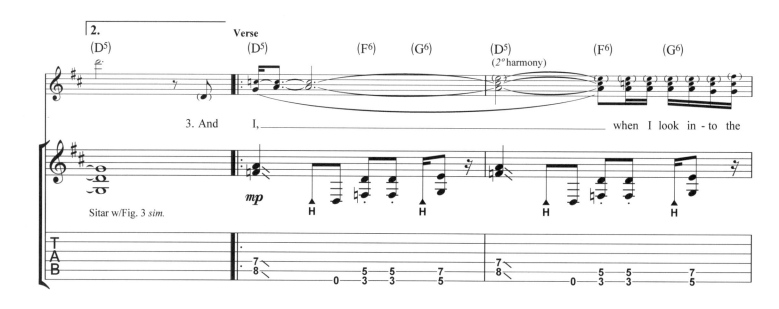

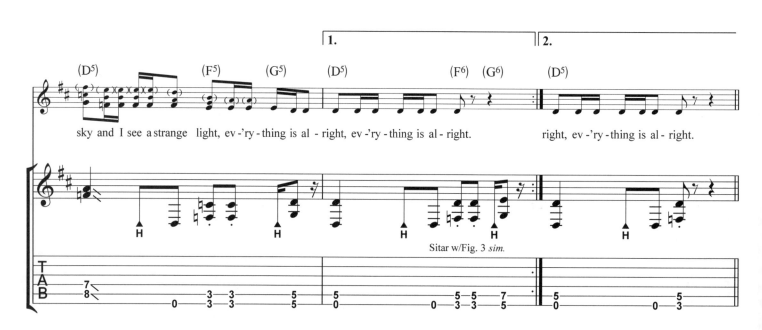

Outro Chorus

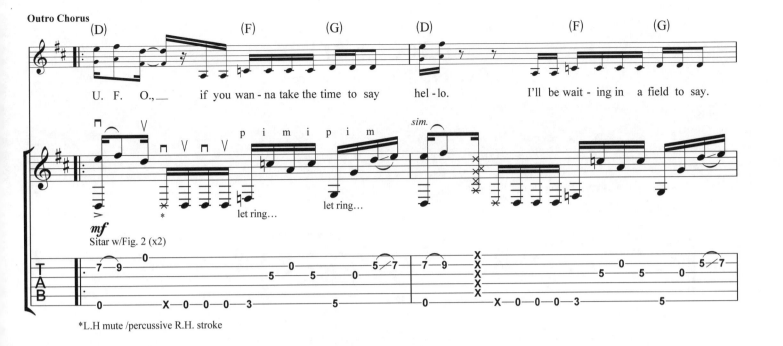

U. F. O.,__ if you wan - na take the time to say hel - lo. I'll be wait - ing in a field to say.

Sitar w/Fig. 2 (x2)

let ring… *let ring…* *sim.*

*L.H mute /percussive R.H. stroke

1, 2.

U. F. O.,__ if you wan - na take the time to say hel - lo, I'll be wait - ing in line.

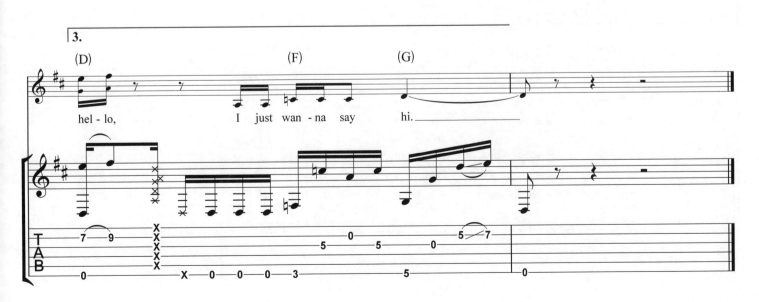

3.

hel - lo, I just wan - na say hi._____

79

face (her)

Words & Music by Newton Faulkner

Tune guitar down a further semitone to match the recording.

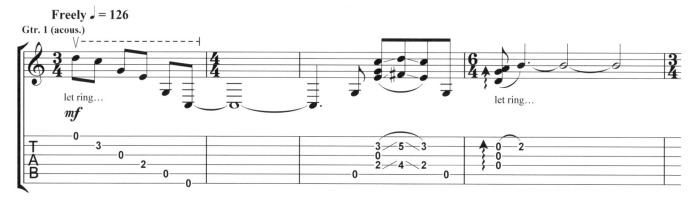

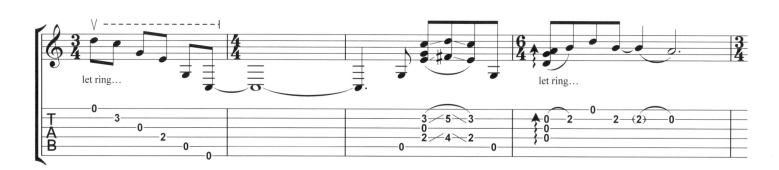

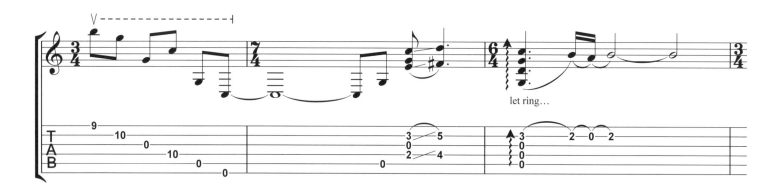

ageing superhero

Words & Music by Newton Faulkner

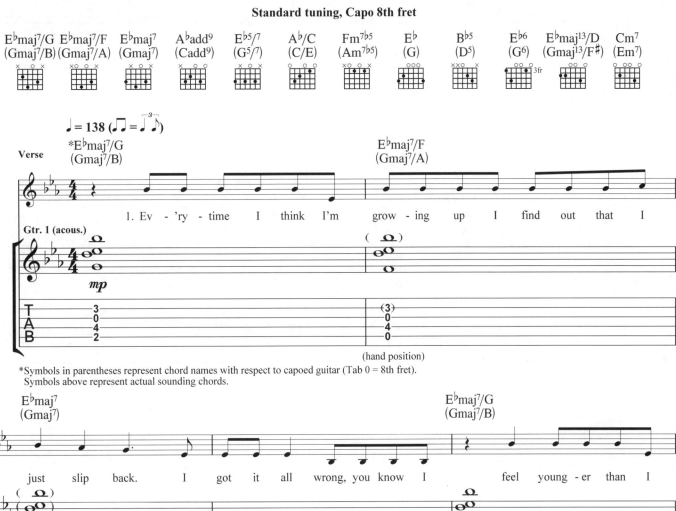

Standard tuning, Capo 8th fret

*Symbols in parentheses represent chord names with respect to capoed guitar (Tab 0 = 8th fret).
 Symbols above represent actual sounding chords.

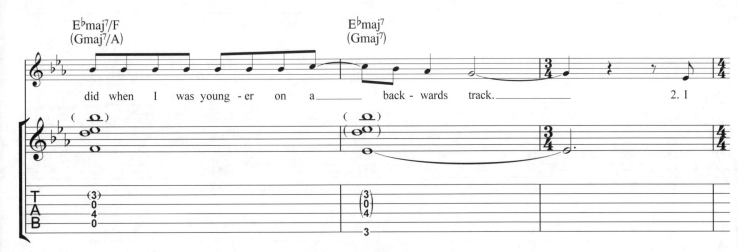

84

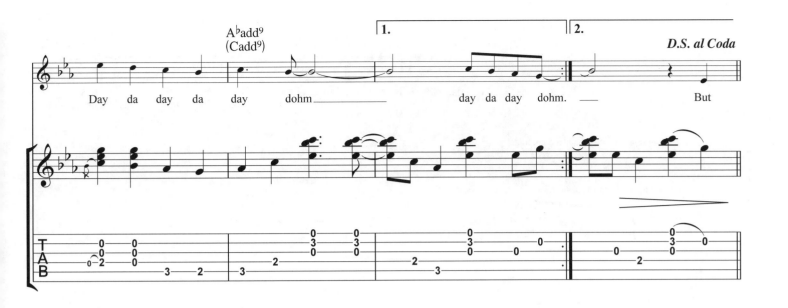

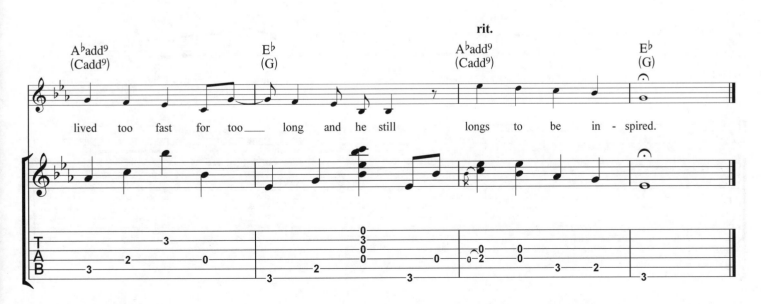

lullaby

Words & Music by Newton Faulkner

Tune guitar down a tone to match recording.

Freely ♩ = 69

Intro

Piano arr. for Gtr, standard tuning

let ring…　　　　　　sim.

p

Close your eyes,＿　　　　　　get some sleep.＿

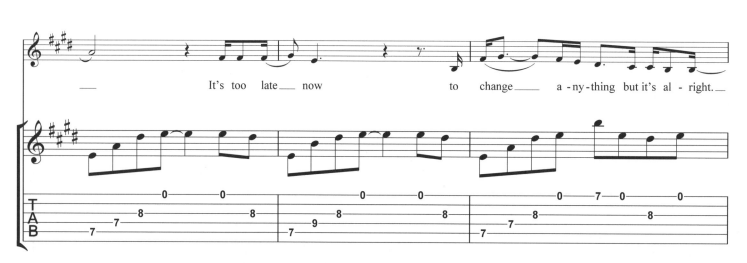

＿　It's too late＿ now　　　to change＿ a-ny-thing but it's al - right.＿

Get some sleep.___ It's so dark out - side_____ so close___

___ your___ eyes and feel the world turn

round. If you're not lost I guess that makes_ you found.___

2 3 4 5 6 7 8 9

4/08(165518)